I
SPY

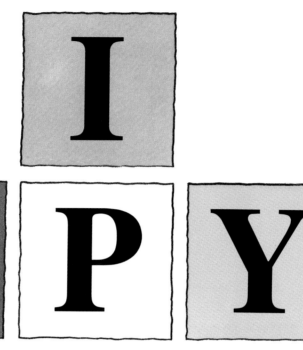

Written by Keith Faulkner

Illustrated by Jonathan Lambert

I spy with my little eye,
Something beginning with P.

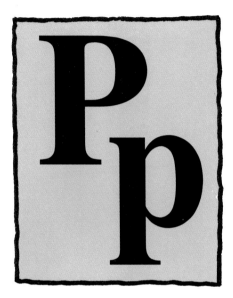

It's almost hidden by the flap,
Whatever could it be?

Can you guess what it could be . . .

I spy with my little eye,
Something beginning with T.

It's hidden underneath the flap,
Whatever could it be?

Try to guess, you mustn't peek . . .

I spy with my little eye,
Something beginning with K.

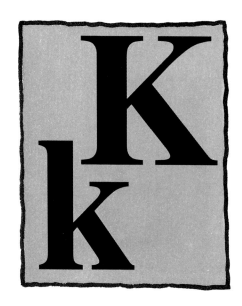

It's almost hidden by the flap,
But see what you would say.

Can you guess or can you see . . .

I spy with my little eye,
Something beginning with F.

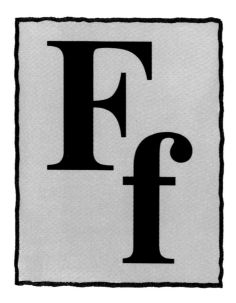

It's almost hidden by the flap,
Whatever could it be?

Try to guess, you must not look . . .

I spy with my little eye,
Something beginning with G.

They're almost hidden by the flap,
Whatever could they be?

Can you guess what they could be . . .

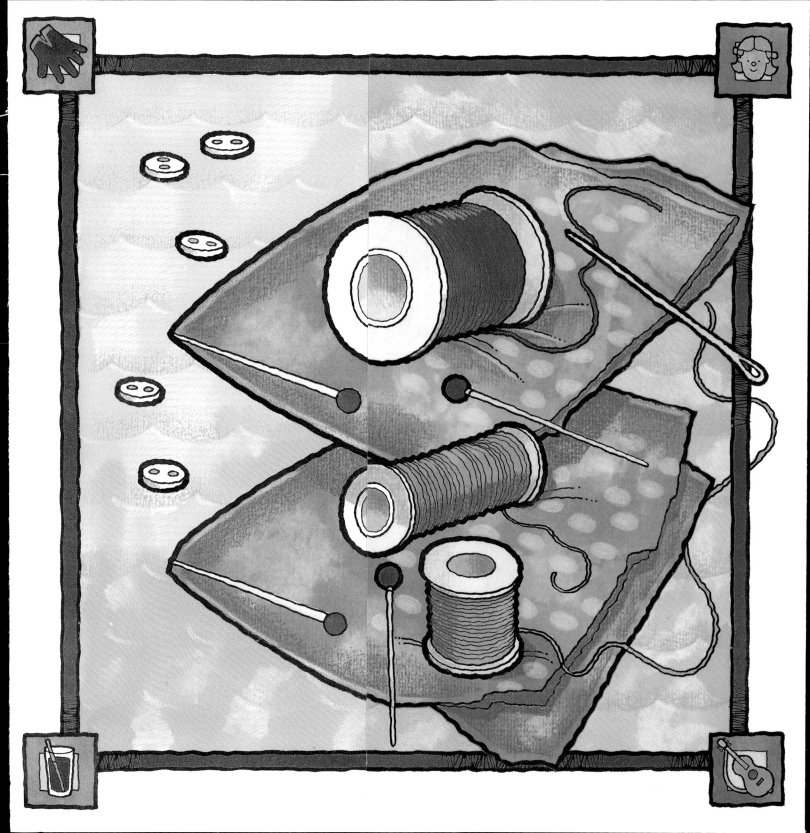

P g K

I spy with my little eye,
Each page is a big surprise.
Why don't you take another look,
You won't believe your eyes.

T k f